The BASEBALL WIZ Trivia QUIZ

by Harry Patterson

RED-LETTER PRESS, INC.

THE BASEBALL WIZ TRIVIA QUIZ
Copyright ©2001 Red-Letter Press, Inc.
ISBN: 0-940462-51-6
All Rights Reserved
Printed in the United States of America

For information address:

Red-Letter Press, Inc.
P.O. Box 393, Saddle River, NJ 07458

ACKNOWLEDGMENTS

Cover design
and typography: s.w.artz, inc.

Editorial: Ellen Fischbein

Contributors: Angela Demers
Jack Kreismer
Tom Lehmann
Mike Ryan

DEDICATION

For my cousin Jack,
Who saw the Waner brothers,
Pie Traynor, Hack Wilson,
Ruth, Gehrig, DiMaggio,
Kiner and Clemente
(among others) play.

SPECIAL THANKS TO:

Jack Fierst
Bill Moushey
Mike Ryan
Dave Smith
The Staff at the Shaler North Hills Library
The Gang at the Shaler Lounge
The Gang at the River City Inn

INTRODUCTION

Red-Letter Press proudly steps up to the plate with *The Baseball Wiz Trivia Quiz*. Formatted in ten-question quizzes, it features an all-star selection of hardball trivia.

Harry Patterson brings you a book interspersed with quips and quotes and loaded with stumpers … Who was the first designated hitter to play in all 162 games? … What was the very first team Sammy Sosa played for? … Which two players reached the 3,000 hit plateau on consecutive days in 1999?

The answers are all inside. Now let's find out if you're a baseball wiz or wannabe.

Jack Kreismer
Publisher

FIRST OF ALL

1. If every one of the thousands of names which appeared in a major league box score in the 1900s were listed alphabetically, which name would be first?

2. Where and when was the first night game in major league history?

3. Where and when was the first World Series night game?

4. Who was the first Rookie of the Year?

5. Who was the first black to coach in the majors?

6. Who was the first black American Leaguer?

7. Who were the first two black managers to face each other in a regular season game?

8. What was the first ballpark built with steel as a primary component?

9. Who was the first designated hitter to step up to the plate?

10. Who was the first DH to play in all 162 games?

Sec. **82**   Row **E**   Seat **17**

Enter Gate B

"In 1962, I was voted Minor League Player of the Year. Unfortunately, that was my second year in the majors."

–Broadcaster and former player Bob Uecker

ANSWERS

1. Henry Aaron — He's first on a couple of other lists too.

2. May 24, 1935 at Cincinnati's Crosley Field — Reds over Phillies, 2-1

3. October 13, 1971 at Pittsburgh's Three Rivers Stadium — Pirates over Orioles in game four

4. Jackie Robinson in 1947 — Separate league selections didn't begin until 1949.

5. Buck O'Neil for the Cubs in 1962

6. Larry Doby with the Indians — 11 weeks after Jackie Robinson in the National League

7. Frank Robinson, Orioles and Cito Gaston, Blue Jays in 1989

8. Pittsburgh's Forbes Field, 1909-70

9. Ron Blomberg of the Yankees

10. Rusty Staub of the Tigers, 1978

FULL SEASON

Sec. 17
Row K
Seat 22
Gate F

"It's what you learn after you know it all that counts."

–Orioles manager Earl Weaver

DEUCES

1. Many teams have had two players with the same last name, but the '62 expansion Mets had two with the same first and last names. Who were they?

2. Which two Red Sox battled it out for '75 Rookie of the Year?

3. Which two future Hall of Famers reached the 3000 hit plateau on consecutive days in 1999?

4. Name the two pitchers who collaborated on a combined extra inning no-hitter in 1997.

5. In their first season in Milwaukee (1953), the Braves featured the league's leading home run hitter and the pitcher with the league's most wins. Who were they?

6. The National Leagues' first two black managers took over their teams at the start of the 1993 season. Who were they?

7. In what offensive category is Tris Speaker the all-time leader with 792?

8. On June 28, 1986 two 300 game winners started against each other, the first time this happened. Who were they?

9. Which two Yankees both homered, in the same game, from both sides of the plate in 2000, the first teammates to do so?

10. Two guys named Edwin were first and third in homers hit during the '50s. Who were they?

ANSWERS

1. The two Bob Millers

2. Jim Rice and Fred Lynn — Lynn won.

3. Tony Gwynn and Wade Boggs

4. The Pirates' Francisco Cordova and Ricardo Rincon — vs. the Astros in Pittsburgh in 1997

5. Eddie Mathews, 47 homers and Warren Spahn, 23 wins

6. Don Baylor, Rockies and Dusty Baker, Giants

7. Doubles

8. Phil Niekro, Indians and Don Sutton, Angels

9. Bernie Williams and Jorge Posada

10. Duke Snider with 326 and Eddie Mathews with 299 — Gil Hodges was second with 310.

Sec. 07

Row 19

Seat 12

Enter
Gate C

Upper Tier

"My autograph may not be worth much now, but five years from now it will be worth even less."

–Tommy Lasorda

FULL SEASON TICKET

THREES

1. Which three offensive categories constitute baseball's Triple Crown?

2. Which three categories make up the Triple Crown for pitchers?

3. The Cubs' Jimmy Cooney, the Red Sox' John Valentin and the Phillies' Mickey Morandini are three of only ten players in the 1900s to perform one of the rarest feats in baseball. What is it?

4. On October 2, 1920 the Pirates and Reds did something that was done only once in the 1900s. What was it?

5. One team has won the World Series representing three different cities. Name the team and the cities.

6. Name the three teams that all-time hits leader Pete Rose played for.

7. Which three Dodger pitchers gave up Reggie Jackson's three homers in game six of the 1977 World Series?

8. Which three players each homered in a record eight consecutive games in the 1900s?

9. Name the three brothers who appeared in the same outfield in a single game in 1962.

10. He had two fingers on his throwing hand mangled in a childhood accident. Ironically this later helped him get movement on his pitches as a pro. Name this Hall of Famer.

ANSWERS

1. Average, home runs and RBIs

2. Wins, ERA and strikeouts

3. Turning an unassisted triple play

4. Played a tripleheader

5. The Braves of Boston in 1914, Milwaukee in 1957 and Atlanta in 1995

6. The Reds, Phillies and Expos

7. Burt Hooten, Elias Sosa and Charlie Hough

8. Dale Long — Pirates, 1956; Don Mattingly — Yankees, 1987; and Ken Griffey Jr. — Mariners, 1993

9. Matty, Felipe and Jesus Alou

10. Mordecai "Three Finger" Brown

"Back then, if you had a sore arm, the only people concerned were you and your wife. Now, it's you, your wife, your agent, your investment counselor, your stockbroker, and your publisher."

–Jim Bouton

Sec. 16

Row 51

Seat 7a

Enter Gate G

Lower Tier

FOURS

1. Boston's Pedro Martinez struck out the first four batters he faced in the 1999 All-Star Game. Who were they?

2. Name the four major league teams for which the legendary Harry Carey worked in the broadcast booth.

3. Name the four teams Reggie Jackson played for.

4. Name the four 20-game winners for the 1971 Orioles.

5. Name the four 20-game winners for the 1920 White Sox, two of whom were later implicated in the Black Sox scandal.

6. Name the four Robinsons in the Hall of Fame.

7. How does a batter "hit for the cycle"?

8. In 1961 Roger Maris hit 61 homers and Mickey Mantle hit 54. Do you know the four other Yanks who also hit 20 or more that year?

9. Can you name the Dodgers all-switch-hitter infield of 1965?

10. Name the four skippers to manage both the Yankees and the Mets.

ANSWERS

1. Barry Larkin, Larry Walker, Sammy Sosa and Mark McGwire

2. The Cardinals, the Oakland A's, the White Sox and, oh yes, the Cubs

3. The A's — in both KC and Oakland, the Orioles, the Yankees and the Angels

4. Jim Palmer, Dave McNally, Mike Cueller and Pat Dobson

5. Red Faber, Eddie Ciccote, Lefty Williams and Dickie Kerr

6. Jackie, Frank, Brooks and Wilbert, who managed the Brooklyn Dodgers, 1914-31 and was a catcher, mostly with the old Baltimore Orioles

7. By hitting a single, double, triple and home run in the same game, not necessarily in that order

8. Moose Skowron — 28, Yogi Berra — 22, Elston Howard — 21 and John Blanchard — 21

9. 1B — Wes Parker, 2B — Jim Lefebvre, SS — Maury Wills and 3B — Jim Gilliam

10. Casey Stengel, Yogi Berra, Dallas Green and Joe Torre

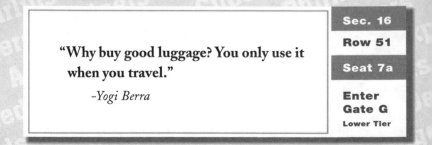

"Why buy good luggage? You only use it when you travel."

-Yogi Berra

Sec. 16

Row 51

Seat 7a

Enter Gate G
Lower Tier

FIVES

1. Name the five pitchers to face both Mark McGwire and Roger Maris.

2. Who were the five charter inductees into the Hall of Fame?

3. Name the five future Hall of Famers struck out in succession by the Giants' Carl Hubbell in the 1934 All-Star Game.

4. Five Cy Young Award winners are convicted felons. How many can you name?

5. Name the top five sluggers on the all-time career home run list at the end of the 1900s.

6. Five managerial careers touched their fourth decade on Opening Day 2000. Can you name these five skippers?

7. Name the five National League teams to play in three centuries while continuously representing the same cities.

8. Name the five current MLB teams named not for cities, but for states.

9. In which city is the home field of each located?

10. Name the top five pitchers in all-time career victories. (We won't be needing any end-of-the-1900s qualifier here — or probably ever.).

ANSWERS

1. Tommy John, Nolan Ryan, Don Sutton, Joe Niekro and Phil Niekro

2. Babe Ruth, Christy Mathewson, Honus Wagner, Ty Cobb and Walter Johnson

3. Babe Ruth, Lou Gehrig, Jimmy Foxx, Al Simmons and Joe Cronin

4. Dwight Gooden, Lamarr Hoyt, Denny McLain, Vida Blue and Fergie Jenkins

5. Henry Aaron — 755, Babe Ruth — 714, Willie Mays — 660, Frank Robinson — 586 and Harmon Killebrew — 573

6. Bobby Cox, Tony LaRussa, Jack McKeon, Jim Fregosi and Joe Torre

7. The Cubs, Reds, Cardinals, Pirates and Phillies

8. Minnesota Twins, Texas Rangers, Colorado Rockies, Florida Marlins and Arizona Diamondbacks

9. Twins — Minneapolis, Rangers — Arlington, Rockies — Denver, Diamondbacks — Phoenix and Marlins — Miami

10. Cy Young — 511, Walter Johnson — 417, Christy Mathewson — 373, Grover Cleveland Alexander — 373 and Warren Spahn — 363

GETTING STARTED

What was the very first major league team
each of the following played for?

1. Babe Ruth

2. Sammy Sosa

3. Tommy John

4. Honus Wagner

5. Roger Maris

6. Nolan Ryan

7. Steve Carlton

8. Jim Kaat

9. Orlando Cepeda

10. Joe Niekro

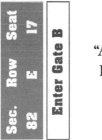

Sec.	Row	Seat
82	E	17

Enter Gate B

"Age is a question of mind over matter.
If you don't mind, age don't matter."

–Hall of Fame pitcher Satchel Paige

ANSWERS

1. Red Sox, 1914
2. Texas Rangers, 1989
3. Indians, 1963
4. Louisville Colonels, 1897
5. Indians, 1957
6. Mets, 1966
7. Cardinals, 1965
8. Senators, 1959
9. Giants, 1958
10. Cubs, 1967

"Baseball is a game where a curve is an optical illusion, a screwball can be a pitch or a person, stealing is legal and you can spit anywhere you like except in the umpire's eye or on the ball."

–Sportswriter Jim Murray

Sec. 16

Row 51

Seat 7a

Enter
Gate G
Lower Tier

DECADES OF DINGERS

Do you know who hit the most home runs during each decade
of the last century? You're excused for not knowing the '00s
and the teens but you'd better know the '20s and the '90s.
The decade and number of homers are provided.

1. '00s — 67
2. '10s — 116
3. '20s — 467
4. '30s — 415
5. '40s — 234
6. '50s — 326
7. '60s — 393
8. '70s — 296
9. '80s — 313
10. '90s — 404

FULL SEASON

Sec. 17
Row K
Seat 22
Gate F

"Going to bed with a woman never hurt a
ball player. It's staying up all night looking
for them that does you in."

–*Casey Stengel*

ANSWERS

1. Harry Davis
2. Gavvy Cravath
3. Babe Ruth
4. Jimmie Foxx
5. Ted Williams
6. Duke Snider
7. Harmon Killebrew
8. Willie Stargell
9. Mike Schmidt
10. Mark McGwire

Sec.	Row	Seat	
82	E	17	Enter Gate B

"It isn't the high price of stars that's so expensive, it's the high price of mediocrity."

–Former owner Bill Veeck

"THE" NICKNAMES

Name the baseballer for each of "the" following nicknames.

1. The Barber
2. The Kitten
3. The Cat
4. The Man
5. The Mad Hungarian
6. The Yankee Clipper
7. The Hat
8. The Deacon
9. The Sultan of Swat
10. The Lip

"The last time the Cubs won a World Series was in 1908. The last time they were in one was in 1945. Hey, any team can have a bad century."

–Cubs manager Tom Trebelhorn

Sec. 16

Row 51

Seat 7a

Enter
Gate G
Lower Tier

ANSWERS

1. Sal Maglie
2. Harvey Haddix
3. Harry Brecheen
4. Stan Musial
5. Al Hrabosky
6. Joe DiMaggio
7. Harry Walker
8. Vernon Law
9. Babe Ruth
10. Leo Durocher

"I knew it was going to be a long season when, on opening day during the national anthem, one of my players turns to me and says, 'Every time I hear that song, I have a bad game.'"

–Former Pirates manager Jim Leyland

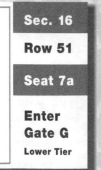

Sec. 16

Row 51

Seat 7a

Enter Gate G

Lower Tier

BASEBALL BAFFLERS

1. The Atlanta Braves, the so-called "Team of the '90s", won eight division championships and five pennants during that decade. How many World Series did they win?

2. One of baseball's oldest single-season hitting records was officially changed in 1999 due to a newly discovered scoring error. What was the record?

3. Which two players with similar sounding names shared the 1975 All-Star Game MVP?

4. Greg Maddux began wearing them in the '90s. In 1915 the Cards' Lee Meadows was the first major-leaguer of the 1900s to wear them. What are they?

5. In 1999 two Devil Rays teammates became the first to each hit 30 homers for four different teams. Who are they?

6. What is the oldest continuously operating franchise in pro sports history?

7. Barry Bonds played in exactly 2,000 games at the end of 1999. Did he play more for the Giants, Pirates or 1,000 each?

8. Who had the record for consecutive games played in the National League when American Leaguer Lou Gehrig's streak ended at 2,130 in 1939?

9. Two All-Star Games were played each year from 1959-62. Which NL pitcher started both games in 1959?

10. How many times was Billy Martin hired and fired as manager of the Yankees?

ANSWERS

1. One, 1995

2. Hack Wilson's 190 RBIs in 1930 was increased by one.

3. The Cub's Bill Madlock and the Met's Jon Matlack

4. Glasses

5. Jose Canseco, who did it previously with the A's, Rangers and Blue Jays and Fred McGriff who did it with the Blue Jays, Padres and Braves

6. The Atlanta Braves — They began as the Boston Red Stockings of the National Association in 1871 and never missed a season.

7. He played 1,010 for the Pirates and 990 for the Giants.

8. The Pirates' Gus Suhr with 822, in 1931-37, still ninth all-time

9. The Dodgers' Don Drysdale

10. Five

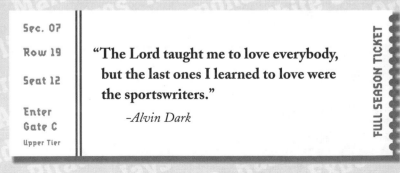

Sec. 07

Row 19

Seat 12

Enter
Gate C
Upper Tier

"The Lord taught me to love everybody, but the last ones I learned to love were the sportswriters."

–Alvin Dark

FULL SEASON TICKET

TEAM SOBRIQUETS

Below are ten nicknames that apply to teams, usually of a certain year or era. To which teams do each refer?

1. The Black Sox
2. America's Team
3. The Whiz Kids
4. The Wheeze Kids
5. Harvey's Wallbangers
6. The Hitless Wonders
7. The Gas House Gang
8. The Fam-a-lee
9. Dem Bums
10. The Big Red Machine

"If a woman has to choose between catching a fly ball and saving an infant's life, she will choose to save the infant's life without even considering if there are men on base."

–Dave Barry

Sec. 16

Row 51

Seat 7a

Enter
Gate G

Lower Tier

ANSWERS

1. White Sox — The name became synonymous with the 1919 scandal but originated a year earlier from the dirty uniforms that owner Charles Comiskey refused to pay to clean.

2. Atlanta Braves — self-named because their games aired on owner Ted Turner's cable "Superstation"

3. Philadelphia Phillies — 1950 pennant winners, for their relative youth

4. Phillies — 1983 for their relative "experience"

5. Milwaukee Brewers — manager Harvey Kuenn's 1982 power-hitting pennant winners

6. Chicago White Sox — 1906 World Champs despite a team batting average of .230

7. St. Louis Cardinals — 1930, various accounts

8. Pittsburgh Pirates — Willie Stargell led the 1979 World Champs for the team anthem *We Are Family* by Sister Sledge.

9. Brooklyn Dodgers — from 1889-1955

10. Cincinnati Reds — for nearly all of the '70s

FRIENDLY FACILITIES

1. Which park saw its final game in 1999 despite an $8 million facelift in 1993?

2. Name the three rivers of Pittsburgh's Three Rivers Stadium.

3. Which two ballparks are nicknamed "The Bob" and "The Ted"?

4. Which ballpark never saw a no-hitter in its more than 60 years of existence?

5. Yankee Stadium underwent a two year renovation in 1974-75. Where did the Yanks play their home games during those two seasons?

6. Which is older, Wrigley Field or Fenway Park?

7. In 1997 Miami's Pro Player Stadium became the fourth facility to host both a World Series and a Super Bowl. Can you name the first three?

8. The Mets moved to Shea Stadium in their third year. Where did they play during their first two seasons?

9. As a way around the nasty meteorological situation, which park regularly hosted more day games than any facility except Wrigley Field?

10. Name the three way-too-similar, now obsolete multi-purpose "cookie-cutter" stadiums that opened in the early '70s.

ANSWERS

1. Tiger Stadium

2. The Allegheny and the Monongahela flow into the Ohio.

3. Arizona's Bank One Ballpark and Atlanta's Turner Field, respectively

4. Pittsburgh's Forbes Field

5. Shea Stadium

6. Fenway opened in 1912, Wrigley in 1914 (though the Cubs didn't begin play there until 1916).

7. L.A. Coliseum, San Diego's Jack Murphy Stadium and the Minnesota Metrodome

8. The Polo Grounds

9. San Francisco's Candlestick (or 3Com) Park

10. Cincinnati's Riverfront, Pittsburgh's Three Rivers and Philadelphia's Veterans

Sec.	Row	Seat
82	E	17

Enter Gate B

"A team is where a boy can prove his courage on his own. A gang is where a coward goes to hide."

–Mickey Mantle

WHO 'DAT?

Identify each of the following.

1. At age 46 this Yankee pitched a complete game shutout, the oldest player in history to do so. As if that wasn't enough, it was also his 300th career victory.

2. He was a longtime broadcaster for the Yankees but later became known to a new generation of fans as the voice of *This Week in Baseball*.

3. At .301 he was the sole American Leaguer to hit over .300 in 1968.

4. He is the only player whose 3,000th hit was a home run.

5. He was one of the best defensive infielders of all time but is remembered more for a singular offensive feat, a World Series winning homer.

6. In 1986 he struck out 20 batters in a game, breaking the record of 19 held jointly by Nolan Ryan, Tom Seaver and Steve Carlton.

7. This Chicago Cub set a record when he was intentionally walked five times in a 16-inning game in 1990.

8. His 400th and 500th home runs came in consecutive seasons.

9. He shared the National League MVP with Willie Stargell in 1979.

10. He was the umpire that Pete Rose was suspended for bumping in 1988.

ANSWERS

1. Phil Niekro

2. Mel Allen

3. Carl Yastrzemski (Oakland's Danny Cater was second with .290. The NL had five players over .300.)

4. Wade Boggs

5. Bill Mazeroski

6. Roger Clemens

7. Andre Dawson

8. Mark McGwire, in 1998-99

9. Keith Hernandez

10. Dave Pallone

"I played on clubs in San Diego and Atlanta where everybody liked each other. Everyone went to dinner together. And we finished in last place together."

–Cito Gaston, on team chemistry

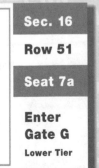

Sec. 16

Row 51

Seat 7a

**Enter
Gate G**
Lower Tier

DECADES OF HITS

Do you know who had the most hits during each decade of the last century? The decade and number of hits are provided.

1. '00s — 1,847
2. '10s — 1,949
3. '20s — 2,085
4. '30s — 1,959
5. '40s — 1,578
6. '50s — 1,875
7. '60s — 1,877
8. '70s — 2,045
9. '80s — 1,731
10. '90s — 1,734

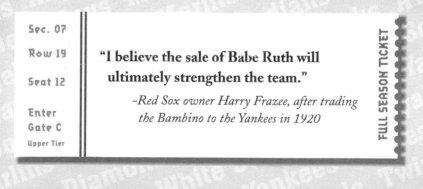

Sec. 07

Row 19

Seat 12

Enter
Gate C

Upper Tier

"I believe the sale of Babe Ruth will ultimately strengthen the team."

–Red Sox owner Harry Frazee, after trading the Bambino to the Yankees in 1920

FULL SEASON TICKET

ANSWERS

1. Honus Wagner
2. Ty Cobb
3. Rogers Hornsby
4. Paul Waner
5. Lou Boudreau
6. Richie Ashburn
7. Roberto Clemente
8. Pete Rose
9. Robin Yount
10. Mark Grace

FULL SEASON

Sec. 17
Row K
Seat 22
Gate F

"I don't want to be a hero; I don't want to be a star. It just works out that way."

–Reggie Jackson

HOMETOWN HEROES

Match each of the following with his birthplace.

1. Nolan Ryan
2. Mickey Mantle
3. Ty Cobb
4. Fergie Jenkins
5. Johnny Bench
6. Willie Stargell
7. Mark McGwire
8. Ken Griffey Sr. & Jr. and Stan Musial
9. Joe DiMaggio
10. Ted Williams

A. Oklahoma City
B. Pomona, California
C. Refugio, Texas
D. Spavinaw, Oklahoma
E. Narrows, Georgia
F. San Diego, California
G. Martinez, California
H. Donora, Pennsysvania
I. Earlsboro, Oklahoma
J. Chatham, Ontario

Sec. Row Seat
82 E 17

Enter Gate B

"This isn't a body. It's a cruel family joke."

–Phillies pitcher Curt Schilling, poking fun at his own physical appearance

ANSWERS

1. C
2. D
3. E
4. J
5. A
6. I
7. B
8. H
9. G
10. F

"It's more relaxed here. It's an atmosphere I can relate to. In Oakland it was always win, win, win and you get fed up with it."

–Jose Canseco, after his move to Texas

Sec. 16

Row 51

Seat 7a

Enter Gate G

Lower Tier

MILESTONES

For which team did …

1. Wade Boggs get his 3000th hit?
2. Eddie Mathews hit his 500th home run?
3. Tom Seaver win his 300th game?
4. Don Sutton win his 300th game?
5. Phil Niekro win his 300th game?
6. Paul Molitor get his 3000th hit?
7. Nolan Ryan win his 300th game?
8. Ty Cobb get his 4000th hit?
9. Pete Rose get his 4000th hit?
10. Babe Ruth get his 700th home run?

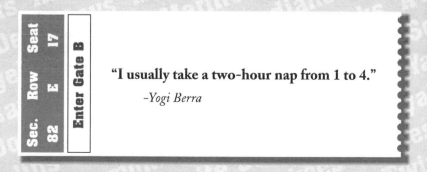

Sec.	Row	Seat
82	E	17

Enter Gate B

"I usually take a two-hour nap from 1 to 4."

–*Yogi Berra*

ANSWERS

1. Devil Rays — 1999
2. Astros — 1967
3. White Sox — 1985
4. Angels — 1986
5. Yankees — 1985
6. Twins — 1996
7. Rangers — 1990
8. Philadelphia Athletics — 1927
9. Expos — 1984
10. Yankees — 1934

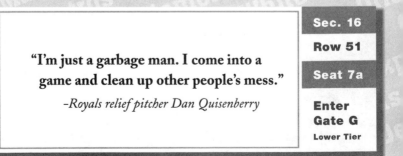

"I'm just a garbage man. I come into a game and clean up other people's mess."

–Royals relief pitcher Dan Quisenberry

Sec. 16

Row 51

Seat 7a

Enter Gate G

Lower Tier

QUOTABLES

Who is quoted in each of the following?

1. "I won't be active in the day-to-day operations of the club at all. I can't spread myself so thin."

2. "I might have had a tough break, but I have an awful lot to live for."

3. "Don't look back. Something might be gaining on you."

4. "It's a great day for baseball. Let's play two."

5. "Say 'Dodgers' and people know you're talkin' about baseball. Say 'Braves' and they ask 'What reservation?' Say 'Reds' and they think of communism. Say 'Padres' and they look around for a priest."

6. "Can't anybody here play this game?"

7. "The next thing you know, they drop the bat down and measure it on home plate. As soon as they did that I said, 'You know, if they call me out, I'll kill them.'"

8. "I acknowledge in the past I have on occasion made insensitive remarks which I know hurt other people. On those occasions it was my mouth but not my heart speaking."

9. "I love the fact that I can go up to the plate and do things right more times than anybody else."

10. "I've only been doing it for 52 years. I think with some experience, I might get a little better."

ANSWERS

1. George Steinbrenner
2. Lou Gehrig
3. Satchel Paige
4. Ernie Banks
5. Tommy Lasorda
6. Casey Stengel, on the hapless expansion Mets
7. George Brett, on the "pine tar" incident
8. Marge Schott
9. Tony Gwynn
10. Harry Carey

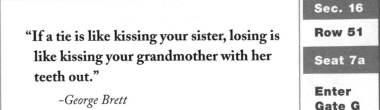

"If a tie is like kissing your sister, losing is like kissing your grandmother with her teeth out."

–George Brett

Sec. 16

Row 51

Seat 7a

Enter Gate G

Lower Tier

RECORD NUMBERS

The following numbers all represent big-time big league records that stood at the end of the 1900s. Some may be breakable, but a few seem to be etched in stone. Can you figure out each record and the player who holds it?

1. 70

2. 755

3. 2,632

4. 56

5. .367

6. 511

7. 4,256

8. 5,714

9. 191

10. 130

FULL SEASON

Sec. 17
Row K
Seat 22
Gate F

"I'm going to cancel my prescription."

–Red Sox pitcher Bob Stanley, after negative comments written about him in a local paper

ANSWERS

1. Most home runs in a single season — Mark McGwire, 1998

2. Most career home runs — Henry Aaron, 1954-76

3. Most consecutive games played — Cal Ripken Jr., 1982-1998

4. Most consecutive games with a hit — Joe DiMaggio, 1941

5. Highest career batting average — Ty Cobb, 1905-28

6. Most career pitching victories — Cy Young, 1890-1911

7. Most career hits — Pete Rose, 1963-86

8. Most career strikeouts by a pitcher — Nolan Ryan, 1966-93

9. Most RBIs in a single season — Hack Wilson, 1930

10. Most stolen bases in a single season — Rickey Henderson, 1982

Sec. 07

Row 19

Seat 12

Enter
Gate C
Upper Tier

FULL SEASON TICKET

"There are two ways to catch a knuckleball. Unfortunately, neither of them works."

–Hitting instructor Charlie Lau

NAME THAT PARK

For a variety of reasons many baseball venues have undergone name changes over the years. Can you match the named facilities with the renamed facilities?

1. Joe Robbie Stadium
2. Weeghman Park
3. Shibe Park
4. Candlestick Park
5. Riverfront Stadium Coliseum
6. Sportsman's Park
7. Briggs Stadium
8. Royals Stadium
9. Jack Murphy Stadium
10. Oakland-Alameda County Coliseum

A. Tiger Stadium
B. Cinergy Field
C. Pro Player Stadium
D. Connie Mack Stadium
E. Network Associates
F. Qualcomm Stadium
G. Kauffman Stadium
H. Busch Stadium
I. 3Com Park
J. Wrigley Field

FULL SEASON	Sec. 17 Row K Seat 22 Gate F	"Ninety feet between home plate and first base may be the closest man has ever come to perfection." *–Sportswriter Red Smith*

ANSWERS

1. C
2. J
3. D
4. I
5. B
6. H
7. A
8. G
9. F
10. E

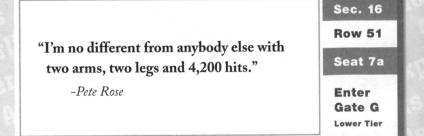

"I'm no different from anybody else with
two arms, two legs and 4,200 hits."

–Pete Rose

Sec. 16

Row 51

Seat 7a

**Enter
Gate G**
Lower Tier

POLITICALLY CORRECT HARDBALL

1. Name the only U.S. Senator to pitch a perfect game.

2. Who was the Brooklyn Dodger Hall of Famer who worked for New York Governor Nelson Rockefeller and campaigned (somewhat reluctantly) for Richard Nixon in 1968?

3. Which early 20th century baseball legend ran unsuccessfully as a Republican for Allegheny County (Pittsburgh) Sheriff in 1925?

4. He was an original Met as well as a member of the World Champion 1960 Pirates before being elected to the U.S. House of Representatives. Who was he?

5. Name the baseball figure pardoned for a felony conviction by President Reagan during his final days in office.

6. His grandfather threw out the ceremonial first pitch for the first Red Sox game in Fenway Park in 1912. Fifty years later he did the same for the Washington Senators home opener. Who was he?

7. Name the politician and former Cubs radio broadcaster who returned to the booth (TV this time) to do an inning at the 1989 All-Star Game.

8. Who was the first sitting president to attend a World Series game? (Hint: It was a Phillies-Red Sox game.)

9. Name the former president who attended several Braves post-season games as the guest of owner Ted Turner.

10. Who was the presidential candidate who congratulated Hideo Nomo and the "Brooklyn Dodgers" following a no-hitter?

ANSWERS

1. Jim Bunning, with the Phillies in 1964

2. Jackie Robinson

3. Honus Wagner

4. Wilmer "Vinegar Bend" Mizell

5. George Steinbrenner

6. John F. Kennedy — His grandfather was Boston Mayor John "Honey Fitz" Fitzgerald.

7. Ronald Reagan

8. Woodrow Wilson, 1915

9. Jimmy Carter

10. Bob Dole, 1996

Sec. 07

Row 19

Seat 12

Enter
Gate C
Upper Tier

"A hot dog at the ballpark is better than steak at the Ritz."

–Actor Humphrey Bogart

FULL SEASON TICKET

AGES FOR THE AGES

Within a year either way, give the age of each of the following.

1. The Reds' Joe Nuxhall when he pitched in his first major league game

2. Nuxhall when he pitched in his second major league game

3. White Sox Hall of Famer Luke Appling when he homered in the Cracker Jack Old Timers Classic

4. Babe Ruth when he hit #60 in 1927

5. Roger Maris when he hit #61 in 1961

6. Sammy Sosa when he hit #66 in 1998

7. Mark McGwire when he hit #70 in 1998

8. Ty Cobb when he got his last hit

9. Pete Rose when he got his last hit

10. Satchel Paige when he pitched three scoreless innings for the Kansas City A's

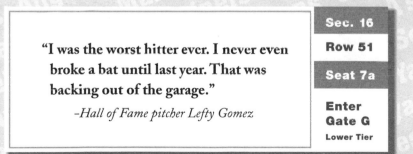

"I was the worst hitter ever. I never even broke a bat until last year. That was backing out of the garage."

–Hall of Fame pitcher Lefty Gomez

Sec. 16

Row 51

Seat 7a

Enter Gate G

Lower Tier

ANSWERS

1. 15
2. 24
3. 75
4. 32
5. 27
6. 29
7. 35
8. 41
9. 45
10. 59 (at least)

Sec. 82 Row E Seat 17 Enter Gate B

"You never know with these psychosomatic injuries. You have to take your time with them."

–Hall of Fame pitcher Jim Palmer

MONIKERS

Identify each of the following by his nickname.

1. Dr. Strangeglove
2. Double X
3. Rapid Robert
4. Stan the Man Unusual
5. Sudden Sam
6. Le Grande Orange
7. Sweet Lou
8. Oil Can
9. Marvelous Marv
10. Dr. K

FULL SEASON

Sec. 17
Row K
Seat 22
Gate F

"If he raced his pregnant wife, he'd finish third."

–Tommy Lasorda, about the slow-footed Dodgers catcher Mike Scioscia

ANSWERS

1. Dick Stuart
2. Jimmie Foxx
3. Bob Feller
4. Don Stanhouse
5. Sam McDowell
6. Rusty Staub
7. Lou Piniella
8. Dennis Boyd
9. Marv Throneberry
10. Dwight Gooden

Sec. 07

Row 19

Seat 12

Enter
Gate C

Upper Tier

"Throwing a fastball past Hank Aaron is like trying to sneak the sun past a rooster."

–Phillies pitcher Curt Simmons

FULL SEASON TICKET

SCREEN TEST

Match the actor with the ballplayer he played in either a TV or theatrical biopic.

1. Louis Gossett Jr.
2. Paul Winfield
3. LaVar Burton
4. Anthony Perkins
5. Dan Dailey
6. Jimmy Stewart
7. Tommy Lee Jones
8. Gary Cooper
9. Stephen Lang
10. Keith Carradine

A. Dizzy Dean
B. Satchel Paige
C. Ron LeFlore
D. Pete Gray
E. Babe Ruth
F. Ty Cobb
G. Roy Campanella
H. Jimmy Piersall
I. Lou Gehrig
J. Monty Stratton

"I retired to go to work. How many people can say that?"

–Former pitcher Gaylord Perry

Sec. 1G

Row 51

Seat 7a

**Enter
Gate G**
Lower Tier

ANSWERS

1. B — *Don't Look Back*, TV, 1981
2. G — *It's Good to Be Alive*, TV, 1974
3. C — *One in a Million: The Ron LeFlore Story*, TV, 1978
4. H — *Fear Strikes Out*, 1957
5. A — *Pride of St. Louis*, 1952
6. J — *The Stratton Story*, 1949
7. F — *Cobb*, 1994
8. I — *The Pride of the Yankees*, 1942
9. E — *Babe Ruth*, TV, 1991
10. D — *A Winner Never Quits*, TV, 1986

Sec. Row Seat
82   E   17
Enter Gate B

"Talent always beats experience. Because by the time you get experience, the talent's gone."

–Indians manager Pat Corrales

WHO YOU TALKIN' 'BOUT?

Below are ten quotes and the person quoted.
Can you figure out who each was talking about?

1. "I can go anywhere he can go in that Rolls Royce."
   —*Enos Slaughter, who played in '40s and '50s, on the lifestyle of a certain '70s superstar*

2. "He was a moody guy, a tantrum thrower like me, but when he punched a locker or something he always did it with his right hand. He was a careful tantrum thrower." —*Ted Williams*

3. "[He] probably gave me more trouble than any other left-handed pitcher." —*Ty Cobb*

4. "We finished last with you. We can finish last without you."
   —*Branch Rickey, then GM of the Pirates*

5. "Just to have his body, I'd trade mine and my wife's and throw in some cash." —*Pete Rose*

6. "Our similarities are different." —*Dale Berra*

7. "He was able to get 25 guys pointed in the same direction, and that direction was winning." —*Joe Morgan*

8. "What Gehrig, Ruth, DiMaggio and Mantle were in their day, that is what [he] is to me." —*George Steinbrenner*

9. "Nothing is more limited than being a limited partner of [his]." —*John McMullen*

10. "I do feel that baseball is really the one thing that if it was taken away from [her] would crush her — other than her dog." —*Barry Larkin*

ANSWERS

1. Reggie Jackson
2. Lefty Grove
3. Babe Ruth
4. Ralph Kiner
5. Mike Schmidt
6. Dale was referring to that master of malaprops, his father, Yogi
7. Sparky Anderson
8. Don Mattingly
9. George Steinbrenner
10. Marge Schott

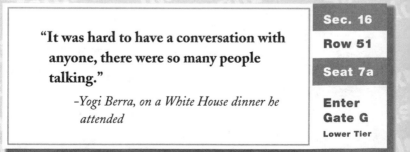

"It was hard to have a conversation with anyone, there were so many people talking."

–Yogi Berra, on a White House dinner he attended

Sec. 16

Row 51

Seat 7a

Enter Gate G
Lower Tier

RAIN DELAY READINGS

Match the baseball tome with its author.

1. *Baseball Is a Funny Game*
2. *The Umpire Strikes Back*
3. *The Bronx Zoo*
4. *The Boys of Summer*
5. *The Summer Game*
6. *The Natural*
7. *Bang the Drum Slowly*
8. *Shoeless Joe* (basis for *Field of Dreams*)
9. *How Life Imitates the World Series*
10. *Strike Zone*

A. W.P. Kinsella
B. Roger Kahn
C. Joe Garagiola
D. Ron Luciano
E. Mark Harris
F. Jim Bouton
G. Roger Angell
H. Thomas Boswell
I. Bernard Malumud
J. Sparky Lyle

FULL SEASON

Sec. 17
Row K
Seat 22
Gate F

"Next up is Fernando Gonzalez, who isn't playing tonight."

–Padres broadcaster Jerry Coleman

ANSWERS

1. C
2. D
3. J
4. B
5. G
6. I
7. E
8. A
9. H
10. F

Sec. 07

Row 19

Seat 12

Enter
Gate C
Upper Tier

"One thing you learn as a Cubs fan: when you buy your ticket, you can bank on seeing the bottom of the ninth inning."

–Broadcaster and former catcher Joe Garagiola

FULL SEASON TICKET

DECADES OF "W"s

Can you name the pitcher with the most wins in each decade of the last century? The decade and the number of victories are provided.

1. '00s — 236
2. '10s — 265
3. '20s — 190
4. '30s — 199
5. '40s — 170
6. '50s — 202
7. '60s — 191
8. '70s — 186
9. '80s — 162
10. '90s — 176

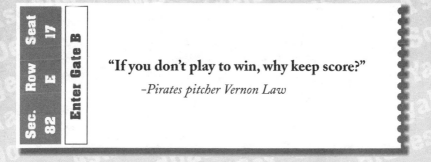

Sec. 82   Row E   Seat 17

Enter Gate B

"If you don't play to win, why keep score?"

–Pirates pitcher Vernon Law

ANSWERS

1. Christy Mathewson
2. Walter Johnson
3. Burleigh Grimes
4. Lefty Grove
5. Hal Newhouser
6. Warren Spahn
7. Juan Marichal
8. Jim Palmer
9. Jack Morris
10. Greg Maddux

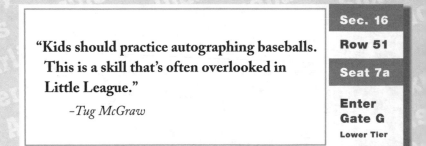

"Kids should practice autographing baseballs. This is a skill that's often overlooked in Little League."

–Tug McGraw

Sec. 16

Row 51

Seat 7a

Enter Gate G
Lower Tier

DINGERS

1. What 68-year-old record did Mark McGwire break with his 57th homer in 1998?

2. Who was third in homers behind McGwire and Sammy Sosa for the 1998 season?

3. McGwire set the record for homers by a rookie in 1987. How many?

4. At which facility did Henry Aaron hit his 714th homer, which tied Babe Ruth on the all-time list?

5. How many times was Roger Maris intentionally walked in 1961, the year he hit 61 homers?

6. When McGwire hit #70 in 1998, whose single season record did he break?

7. Who was the first slugger with over 400 career homers not to be elected to the Hall of Fame when he became eligible?

8. Which Hall of Famer hit 361 career homers yet struck out only 369 times?

9. Name the only father and son to each have three-homer games.

10. Who was the youngest slugger of the 1900s to amass over 40 homers in a season?

ANSWERS

1. Hack Wilson's National League single season home run mark

2. The Padres' Greg Vaughn with 50

3. 49

4. At Cincinnati's Riverfront Stadium on Opening Day, 1974

5. None — Mickey Mantle followed him in the lineup.

6. His own record of 69, set earlier in the same game

7. Dave Kingman with 442

8. Joe DiMaggio

9. Ken Griffey Sr., 1986 and Jr., 1996

10. Eddie Mathews hit 47 for the Braves in 1953 at age 21.

FULL SEASON

Sec. 17
Row K
Seat 22
Gate F

"The Good Lord was good to me. He gave me a strong body, a good right arm and a weak mind."

—Pitcher Dizzy Dean, upon induction into the Hall of Fame

SHOW BIZ!!!

1. Entertainment legends (and "road" buddies) Bob Hope and Bing Crosby both had ownership stakes in major league teams, often referring to them in their acts. What were the teams?

2. What beloved entertainer was one of the seven original investors in the Seattle Mariners?

3. How is the ending of the movie *The Natural* different from that of the book?

4. Purists had a problem with Ray Liotta's portrayal of Shoeless Joe Jackson in *Field of Dreams*. What was it?

5. Who played Babe Ruth in *The Pride of the Yankees*?

6. Name the Cy Young Award winning pitcher who was cast against type as an intimidating slugger in *Major League*.

7. Which pair played Mr. and Mrs. Grover Cleveland Alexander in *The Winning Team*?

8. On the day of the final episode of TV's *Cheers*, who threw out the ceremonial first pitch at Fenway Park?

9. Which best-selling baseball book was fictionalized into a TV series (starring the author) that had a very brief run in 1976?

10. How was Pete Rose's cameo as Ty Cobb in the TV movie *Babe Ruth* affected by his ban from baseball?

ANSWERS

1. Indians (Hope) and Pirates (Crosby)

2. Danny Kaye

3. Roy Hobbs (Robert Redford) homers in the movie but the character strikes out in the book.

4. Liotta batted right in the movie; the real Jackson batted left.

5. Ruth played himself in the Lou Gehrig biopic.

6. Pete Vuckovich

7. Ronald Reagan and Doris Day

8. John Ratzenberger (Cliff Clavin on the show)

9. *Ball Four*

10. He was forbidden to wear any major league uniform, even that of the '20s Detroit Tigers.

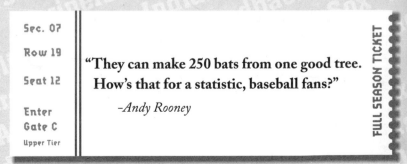

Sec. 07

Row 19

Seat 12

Enter
Gate C

Upper Tier

"They can make 250 bats from one good tree. How's that for a statistic, baseball fans?"

–Andy Rooney

FULL SEASON TICKET

IT'S ALL RELATIVE

1. Which two brothers each hold longtime team records for consecutive games hitting streaks?

2. Name the only two brothers to collaborate on pitching a shutout.

3. Who are the only two brothers in the Hall of Fame as players?

4. Who is Bobby Valentine's father-in-law?

5. Name the brothers who combine for the most career home runs.

6. On which two teams were knuckleballer siblings Phil and Joe Niekro teammates?

7. Which Hall of Famer was Denny McLain's father-in-law?

8. Name the two Yankee pitchers who "swapped wives" in 1973.

9. Name the brothers who combined for most career pitching victories.

10. Name the only two brothers to manage in the bigs at the same time in the 1900s.

ANSWERS

1. Joe (56 for the Yanks) and Dom (34 for the Red Sox) DiMaggio

2. Rick and Paul Reuschel — Cubs over the Dodgers in 1975

3. Paul and Lloyd Waner

4. Ralph Branca

5. Henry and Tommie Aaron with 768 (of which Tommie has 13)

6. Braves, 1973-74 and Yankees, 1985

7. Lou Boudreau

8. Mike Kekich and Fritz Peterson

9. The aforementioned Phil (318) and Joe (221) Niekro with 539

10. Marcel (Angels) and Rene (Marlins) Lachemann in 1995

Sec.	Row	Seat
82	E	17

Enter Gate B

"You can count on the fingers of your right hand the number of times I've hit a homer to the opposite field. About 10."

–*Mets catcher Gary Carter*

FIELDS OF DREAMS

Match the no-longer-with-us ballparks with the once-upon-a-time home teams. (Note: Some parks may have had more than one tenant but each has only one match here.)

1. Forbes Field
2. Polo Grounds
3. Ebbets Field
4. Crosley Field
5. Shibe Park
6. Sportsman's Park
7. Memorial Stadium
8. Griffith Stadium
9. Jarry Park
10. Metropolitan Stadium

A. Pittsburgh Pirates
B. Baltimore Orioles
C. Philadelphia Athletics
D. New York Giants
E. Cincinnati Reds
F. Brooklyn Dodgers
G. Minnesota Twins
H. Montreal Expos
I. St. Louis Browns
J. Washington Senators

FULL SEASON

Sec. 17
Row K
Seat 22
Gate F

"I was just in the right place at the right time."

–Cesar Geronimo, on being strikeout #3,000 for both Bob Gibson and Nolan Ryan

ANSWERS

1. A
2. D
3. F
4. E
5. C
6. I
7. B
8. J
9. H
10. G

"One of my goals in life was to be surrounded by unpretentious, rich young men. Then I bought the Braves and I was surrounded by 25 of them."

–Ted Turner

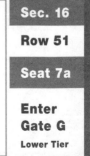

Sec. 16

Row 51

Seat 7a

**Enter
Gate G**

Lower Tier

WHICH ONE WAS IT?

1. He turned an unassisted triple play for the Red Sox in 1923. Was it Jack Benny, George Burns, Bob Hope or Sid Caesar?

2. He played for the 1919 White Sox but was not one of the "eight men out." Was it Richard Pryor, Eddie Murphy, Chris Rock or Tim Meadows?

3. He led the Pirates in homers in 1986. Was it Robbie Krieger, John Densmore, Ray Manzarek or Jim Morrison?

4. He was the first black to play for the Phillies. Was it Dick Nixon, Jimmy Carter, Jerry Ford or John Kennedy?

5. He played parts of five seasons for the Cubs in the '60s and later played for the White Sox, Reds and Astros. Was it Hank Fonda, Jimmy Stewart, John Wayne or Robert Mitchum?

6. He pitched a perfect game for the Rangers in 1994. Was it Willie Nelson, Kenny Rogers, Hank Williams or Glen Campbell?

7. He made it to the majors with the Tigers before going to the World Series with the '86 Mets. Was it Dave Thomas, Roy Rogers, Howard Johnson or Harland Sanders?

8. He was the first DH for the Cubs. Was it Tommy James, Archie Bell, Dave Clark or Ben Folds?

9. He went 18-6 pitching for the '27 Yanks. Was it Flavor Flav, Urban Shocker, Melle Mel or Busta Rhymes?

10. He was the first manager of the A's in Oakland. Was it Ted Kennedy, Bob Kennedy, Jack Kennedy or Joe Kennedy?

ANSWERS

1. George Burns
2. Eddie Murphy
3. Jim Morrison
4. John Kennedy
5. Jimmy Stewart
6. Kenny Rogers
7. Howard Johnson
8. Dave Clark
9. Urban Shocker
10. Bob Kennedy

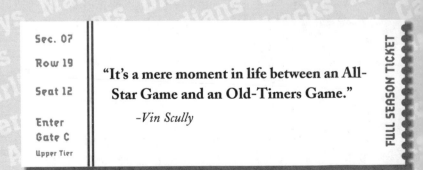

Sec. 07

Row 19

Seat 12

Enter
Gate C
Upper Tier

"It's a mere moment in life between an All-Star Game and an Old-Timers Game."

–Vin Scully

FULL SEASON TICKET

A SIMPLE
YES OR NO WILL DO

1. Is Roger Maris in the Hall of Fame?

2. Did Babe Ruth reach 3,000 hits?

3. Was Ted Williams ever a manager?

4. Rickey Henderson set the single season stolen base record in 1982. Did he ever steal over 100 in a season again?

5. Were Ken Griffey Sr. and Jr. ever teammates?

6. Did the Dodgers retire Jackie Robinson's number before it was retired throughout the majors in 1997?

7. Were Babe Ruth and Joe DiMaggio ever Yankee teammates?

8. Were Joe DiMaggio and Mickey Mantle ever Yankee teammates?

9. Did Reggie Jackson ever play for Kansas City?

10. Did any player other than Pete Rose or Ty Cobb reach the 4,000 hit plateau?

ANSWERS

1. No

2. No — He got 2873.

3. Yes — He helmed the Washington Senators/Texas Rangers from 1969-72.

4. Yes — He stole 108 the following season but never exceeded 100 again.

5. Yes — in 1990-91, with the Mariners

6. Yes — in 1972, the year he died

7. No — Joe came in 1936 and Babe went in 1934.

8. Yes — They overlapped in 1951.

9. Yes — His rookie year was 1967, the A's last in KC.

10. No

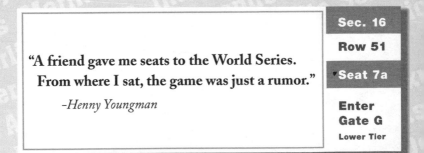

"A friend gave me seats to the World Series. From where I sat, the game was just a rumor."

–*Henny Youngman*

Sec. 16

Row 51

Seat 7a

Enter
Gate G
Lower Tier

AGES FOR THE AGES II

Again, give the age of each of the following
within a year either way.

1. Bill Mazeroski when his homer won the World Series
2. Hack Wilson when he set the single season RBI record
3. Reggie Jackson when he smacked three homers in a World Series game
4. Don Larson when he pitched a perfect World Series game
5. Casey Stengel when he was fired by the Yankees
6. Connie Mack when he managed his final game
7. Kerry Wood when he struck out 20 batters in 1998
8. Willie Stargell during the 1979 World Series
9. Hoyt Wilhelm when he threw his last knuckleball
10. Charlie Hough when he threw his last knuckleball

Sec. 82 Row E Seat 17

Enter Gate B

**"I was thinking of making a comeback, until
I pulled a muscle vacuuming."**

–Johnny Bench

ANSWERS

1. 24
2. 30
3. 31
4. 27
5. 70
6. 87
7. 20
8. 39
9. 48
10. 46

FULL SEASON

Sec. 17
Row K
Seat 22
Gate F

"They told me they wanted me to play it (third base) like Brooks. I did. I played it like Mel Brooks."

–Andy Van Slyke

WHO THREW IT?

Who was the pitcher for each of these
moments in hardball history?

1. Giant Bobby Thomson's "Shot Heard 'Round the World"

2. Henry Aaron's 714th homer, tying Babe Ruth

3. Roger Maris' 61st homer in 1961

4. Babe Ruth's "called shot" against the Cubs in the 1932
World Series

5. Joe Carter's game-winning two-run homer in game six of the
1993 World Series that won it for the Blue Jays

6. Mark McGwire's 61st homer in 1998, tying Roger Maris

7. McGwire's 62nd homer in 1998, breaking Maris' record

8. McGwire's 70th homer in 1998, establishing the new record

9. Ted Williams' 521st and final homer in his final career at-bat

10. George Brett's "pine tar" homer in 1983

ANSWERS

1. Ralph Branca of the Dodgers
2. Jack Billingham of the Reds
3. Tracy Stallard
4. Charlie Root
5. Mitch Williams of the Phillies
6. Mike Korgan of the Cubs
7. Steve Trachsel of the Cubs
8. Carl Pavono of the Expos
9. Jack Fisher of the Orioles
10. Goose Gossage of the Yankees

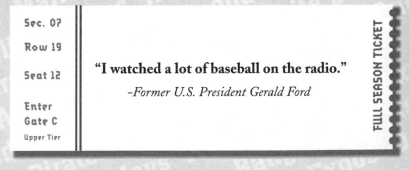

Sec. 07
Row 19
Seat 12
Enter
Gate C
Upper Tier

"I watched a lot of baseball on the radio."

–Former U.S. President Gerald Ford

FULL SEASON TICKET

ON THE FRINGES

Identify the following fringe figures from baseball history.

1. Michael Volpe
2. Johnny Sylvestor
3. Morganna Roberts
4. Steve Dahl
5. Jeffery Maier
6. Ted Giannoulas
7. Howard Spira
8. John Dowd
9. Margo Adams
10. Schotzie and Schotzie 02

"They should move back first base a step
to eliminate all the close plays."

–John Lowenstein

Sec. 16

Row 51

Seat 7a

Enter
Gate G
Lower Tier

ANSWERS

1. The self-proclaimed "free agent fan" who gained a measure of notoriety in 1997 — He chose the Phillies and the AAA Durham Bulls.

2. The bedridden New Jersey youth for whom Babe Ruth may or may not have promised to hit a home run in the 1926 World Series

3. The "Kissing Bandit," who hyped her stripper act by running onto the field and kissing ballplayers in the '70s

4. The Chicago DJ behind the "Disco Demolition" riot that forced the White Sox to forfeit the second game of a doubleheader in 1979

5. The 12-year-old Yankee fan who caught Derek Jeter's homer in the '96 ALCS before Orioles' outfielder Tony Tarasco could get to it

6. The guy in the San Diego chicken suit

7. The gambler whose association with George Steinbrenner led to Steinbrenner's suspension in 1990

8. The former federal prosecutor hired by Major League Baseball to investigate the gambling activities of Pete Rose

9. Wade Boggs' road trip tootsie who later sued him and wrote a book about her exploits

10. Reds owner Marge Schott's two pet St. Bernards that were successive mascots for the team

THE ONLY TIME
IT HAPPENED

1. What is the only occasion in major league history when each and every player on a team began and ended a complete game with the same batting average?

2. Name the only man to wear the uniform of all four New York teams.

3. Hugo Bezdek is the only man to manage a major league team and coach an NFL team. Before coaching the Cleveland Rams in 1937, which baseball team did he manage?

4. Who was the only player of the 1900s to homer in his first two World Series at-bats?

5. Who is the only player to win batting titles in three decades of the 1900s?

6. Who is the only manager to win over 800 games in each league?

7. Who is the only man to have two major league ballparks named after him?

8. Who is the only slugger of the 1900s to hit 50 homers in a season but strike out fewer than 50 times?

9. Who is the only player with at least 100 hits in each of his first 20 seasons?

10. Who is the only player to begin the 2000 season as his 20th consecutive season with the same team?

ANSWERS

1. Indian Bob Feller's opening day no-hitter vs. the White Sox in 1949 — Each Sox player's average remained at .000.

2. Casey Stengel — He played for the Dodgers, 1912-17 and the Giants, 1921-23 and managed the Yankees, 1949-60 and the Mets, 1962-65.

3. The Pirates, 1917-19

4. Gene Tenace of the A's in 1972

5. George Brett in 1976 (.333), 1980 (.390) and 1990 (.329) — all with the Royals

6. Sparky Anderson, 863 with the Reds and 1,331 with the Tigers

7. Charles Comiskey — old and new Comiskey Park

8. The Giants' Johnny Mize in 1947 with 51 homers and only 42 K's

9. Carl Yastrzemski, 1961-80 — The streak was broken only by the '81 strike. He was back on track in 1982 and 1983, his final seasons, thus getting over 100 hits in each of the 22 full seasons he played.

10. Who else but Cal Ripken Jr. with the Orioles?

MONIKERS II

Again, identify the players by the nicknames.

1. Mad Dog
2. Mr. October
3. Scooter
4. Mr. Cub
5. Big Poison
6. Little Poison
7. Pops
8. Country
9. Tom Terrific
10. El Duque

"If horses won't eat it, I don't want to play on it."

–Dick Allen, on artificial turf

ANSWERS

1. Bill Madlock
2. Reggie Jackson
3. Phil Rizzuto
4. Ernie Banks
5. Paul Waner
6. Lloyd Waner
7. Willie Stargell
8. Enos Slaughter
9. Tom Seaver
10. Orlando Hernandez

FULL SEASON   Sec. 17   Row K   Seat 22   Gate F

"The rhythms of the game are so similar to the patterns of American life. Periods of leisure, interrupted by bursts of frantic activity."

–Writer Roger Kahn

TRIVIA ANSWERS

Each of the following major-leaguers is best known today, some perhaps unfairly, as the answer to a trivia question. Do you know the distinction that continues to get each into this and plenty of other trivia books?

1. Wally Pipp
2. Harry Steinfeldt
3. Diego Segui
4. Eddie Gaedel
5. Pete Gray
6. Fred Merkle
7. Carroll Hardy
8. Ray Chapman
9. Francisco Cabrera
10. Johnny Vander Meer

ANSWERS

1. The Yankee first baseman who sat out a game with a minor illness and was replaced by Lou Gehrig, who went on to play the next 2,130 games at that position

2. The third baseman who rounded out the Tinker-to-Evers-to-Chance Cubs infield

3. The journeyman pitcher who is the only man to play for both the Seattle Pilots and Mariners

4. The 3' 7", 65-pound midget who made a single plate appearance for the St. Louis Browns in 1951

5. The one-armed outfielder who played briefly for the Browns in 1945

6. The Giants 19-year-old substitute first baseman whose failure to touch second base in a 1908 game against the Cubs cost his team the pennant

7. The only man to pinch-hit for Ted Williams

8. The Indians shortstop who is the only player to die as a result of an on-field incident (a beanball from the Yankees' Carl Mays)

9. The Braves pinch hitter whose two RBI singles sent the Braves to the World Series and the Pirates home in 1992

10. The Reds pitcher who is the only man to pitch consecutive no-hitters, possibly the most secure record in baseball

BY ANY OTHER NAME

The following are not generally known by their
given first names which are provided in the clues.

1. Lynn struck out his first batter in 1966 and his last in 1993.

2. Vincent missed the 1992 season after undergoing hip
   replacement surgery, returning to the White Sox in 1993.

3. George was one of the best lefties of the teens (1910-19),
   going 86-49 for the Red Sox.

4. Anthony was AL Rookie of the Year with the Red Sox.

5. Denton's 379th career victory was a perfect game.

6. Leroy is a Hall of Fame pitcher with a "lifetime" record of
   28-31. His best work, however, came in the Negro Leagues.

7. Albert managed the Cardinals to a World Championship in
   1967.

8. Commissioner Fay Vincent barred the White Sox from
   placing Saturnino on their active roster in 1990.

9. Harold is fondly remembered for his gesture of putting an
   arm around rookie teammate Jackie Robinson, as well as for
   his Hall of Fame career.

10. Johnnie is often credited with popularizing the "high five"
    with the 70's Dodgers.

ANSWERS

1. Nolan Ryan
2. Bo Jackson
3. Babe Ruth
4. Nomar Garciaparra
5. Cy Young
6. Satchel Paige
7. Red Schoendienst
8. Minnie Minoso
9. Pee Wee Reese
10. Dusty Baker

FULL SEASON

Sec. 17
Row K
Seat 22
Gate F

"If the world were perfect, it wouldn't be."

-Yogi Berra

DIGITAL RETIREMENT

1. Who was the very first major-leaguer to be honored by having his uniform number retired?

2. Whose number is retired by both the Yankees and the Mets?

3. Two teams have each retired a number for two different players. Name the teams, players and numbers.

4. What is the highest number retired for a player?

5. The Pirates retired number 33 for Honus Wagner which he wore as a coach, never as a player. Why?

6. What are the only two single-digit numbers not retired by the Yankees?

7. What was the first of two teams to retire Henry Aaron's number 44?

8. Who was the only Braves player to have his number retired before the team moved to Atlanta?

9. In 1964 Houston retired this pitcher's number after he pitched two seasons for the team with an overall 8-3 record. Who is he?

10. Dave Stewart won 116 games over 1986-92, including four consecutive seasons with 20 or more, for the Oakland A's while wearing number 34. He was reportedly miffed that number 34 was retired in 1993 for which former A's pitcher?

ANSWERS

1. Lou Gehrig — number 4 in 1939

2. Casey Stengel — 37

3. The Yankees retired number 8 for Bill Dickey and Yogi Berra. The Expos retired number 10 for Andre Dawson and Rusty Staub.

4. The White Sox retired number 72 for Carlton Fisk.

5. They didn't wear numbers in Wagner's playing days.

6. 2 and 6

7. The Brewers beat the Braves by a year in 1976.

8. Warren Spahn — 21 — who played for the Braves in both Boston and Milwaukee

9. Reliever Jim Umbricht — He was a solid performer for the expansion club before he died of cancer prior to the 1964 season.

10. Rollie Fingers

Sec. 07

Row 19

Seat 12

Enter
Gate C
Upper Tier

"My ultimate dream is to have my own bank, maybe in Paris. I'd call it, 'Banks' Bank on the Left Bank.'"

–Ernie Banks

FULL SEASON TICKET

THE BRONX BOMBERS

Love 'em or hate 'em, they're probably the only team
deserving of a page of their own.

1. Who played the longest with the Yanks without getting a
   World Series ring?

2. What is the only decade since the teens during which the
   Yankees didn't win a World Series?

3. Who had the most at-bats for the legendary 1927 Yanks?

4. Who is Bob Sheppard?

5. For how many seasons were the Yanks the only team in
   New York?

6. For how much money did George Steinbrenner acquire
   controlling interest in the Yanks in 1972?

7. Which company did Steinbrenner's group buy the team from?

8. For which five seasons was Reggie Jackson a Yankee?

9. Don Larson and David Wells both threw perfect games for
   the Yankees, the former in a World Series game. What other
   remarkable connection do they share?

10. Who was the homer-hitting hero of game three of the
    '99 Series who abruptly blew off post-game interviewer
    Jim Gray?

ANSWERS

1. Don Mattingly, 1982-95

2. The '80s

3. Earl Combs with 648 and a .356 average — Lou Gehrig was second with 584.

4. The longtime PA announcer at Yankee Stadium

5. Four — 1958-61, following the departure of the Giants and Dodgers and before the arrival of the Mets

6. $10 million

7. CBS

8. 1977-81

9. Both attended Point Loma High School in San Diego.

10. Chad Curtis

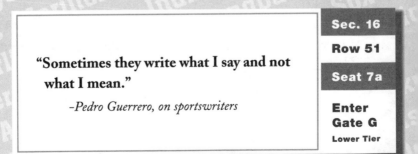

"**Sometimes they write what I say and not what I mean.**"

–Pedro Guerrero, on sportswriters

Sec. 16

Row 51

Seat 7a

Enter
Gate G
Lower Tier

EASY AUTOGRAPHS

The answer to each has a three-letter last name.

1. He threw a no-hitter for the Expos against the Giants in 1981.

2. This Hall of Famer hit 511 career homers, a record when he retired.

3. He took a nasty Goose Gossage beanball in game five of the '81 World Series.

4. The Pirates obtained this infielder from the Astros in 1981 for Phil Garner.

5. He was flaky, but mostly effective, pitching in over 400 games for the Red Sox and Expos over 14 seasons.

6. He was Rookie of the Year for the Dodgers in 1982.

7. He was one of the best lefty starters of the '80s and '90s, first with the Blue Jays, then with the Yankees.

8. This scrappy White Sox second baseman smacked seven consecutive hits against the Yanks in a 1956 doubleheader.

9. He was 1-for-2 as a backup catcher for the Pirates in the 1971 World Series. He went on to play for the Astros, Tigers, White Sox and Giants before returning to Pittsburgh to finish his playing career in 1983-84.

10. This journeyman pitcher spent 18 seasons in the bigs (1965, 1969-83) compiling a 152-156 record mostly with the Angels and Yanks.

ANSWERS

1. Charlie Lea
2. Mel Ott
3. Ron Cey
4. Johnny Ray
5. Bill Lee
6. Steve Sax
7. Jimmy Key
8. Nellie Fox
9. Milt May
10. Rudy May

Sec. | Row | Seat
82 | E | 17

Enter Gate B

"As I remember, the bases were loaded."

*–Phillies outfielder Garry Maddox, describing
his first grand slam*

"THE" NICKNAMES II

Again, give "the" nicknames for each of the following.

1. The Big Train
2. The Bird
3. The Bull
4. The Cobra
5. The Count
6. The Flying Dutchman
7. The Great One
8. The Ol' Perfessor
9. The Penguin
10. The Spaceman

FULL SEASON

Sec. 17
Row K
Seat 22
Gate F

"You know you're having a bad day when
the fifth inning rolls around and they
(the grounds crew) drag the warning track."

–Orioles pitcher Mike Flanagan

ANSWERS

1. Walter Johnson
2. Mark Fidrych
3. Greg Luzinski
4. Dave Parker
5. John Montefusco
6. Honus Wagner
7. Roberto Clemente
8. Casey Stengel
9. Ron Cey
10. Bill Lee

Sec. 07

Row 19

Seat 12

Enter
Gate C
Upper Tier

FULL SEASON TICKET

"My goals are to hit .300, score 100 runs, and stay injury-prone."

–Yankees outfielder Mickey Rivers

NOT HIM

1. Which of the following is not a knuckleballer … Tim Wakefield, Tom Candiotti, Mitch Williams or Charlie Hough?

2. Which player is not in the Hall of Fame … Gaylord Perry, Luis Aparicio, Tommy John or Joe Tinker?

3. Which pitcher never threw a no-hitter … Fernando Valenzuela, Luis Tiant, Terry Mulholland or Hideo Nomo?

4. Which pitcher never won a Cy Young Award … Nolan Ryan, Denny McLain, Doug Drabek or Steve Carlton?

5. Which pitcher never took the mound for the Amazing Mets in 1969 … Don Cardwell, Nolan Ryan, Tug McGraw or Ray Sadecki?

6. Which of the following does not have over 3,000 career hits … Al Kaline, Roberto Clemente, Lou Brock or Paul Waner?

7. Which of the following never appeared in a post-season game … Ernie Banks, Rod Carew, Don Mattingly or Dale Long?

8. Which of the following never played for the White Sox … Ron Santo, Sammy Sosa, Willie Montanez or Johnny Evers?

9. Which slugger does not have over 500 career homers … Willie McCovey, Willie Stargell, Ernie Banks or Jimmie Foxx?

10. Which of the following does not have over 300 career pitching victories … Gaylord Perry, Lefty Grove, Tom Seaver or Steve Carlton?

ANSWERS

1. Williams
2. John
3. Tiant
4. Ryan
5. Sadecki
6. Clemente — He has exactly 3,000.
7. Banks
8. Montanez
9. Stargell
10. Grove — He has exactly 300.

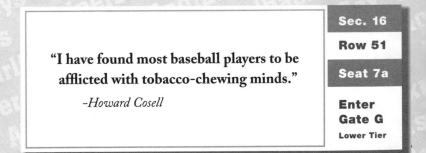

"I have found most baseball players to be afflicted with tobacco-chewing minds."

-Howard Cosell

Sec. 16

Row 51

Seat 7a

**Enter
Gate G**

Lower Tier

THE FALL CLASSIC

1. The first World Series took place in 1903. It has been played every year since with the exception of which two years?

2. The Yankees won three of the last four World Series of the 1900s. Who won the other one?

3. Which two teams played in the first intra-city World Series?

4. True or false? That Series was played on consecutive dates because travel days were unnecessary.

5. What was the last intra-city World Series of the 1900s?

6. The 1914 and 1915 World Series were both Philadelphia vs. Boston affairs, yet no team repeated in 1915. Explain.

7. Which teams faced each other in the first all-California World Series?

8. Which Series was the first to produce seven home-team victories?

9. Which teams played in the "I-70 Series"?

10. Which teams played in the "I-95 Series"?

ANSWERS

1. 1904 when Giants owner John Brush refused to participate and 1994 due to the players' strike

2. The Florida Marlins, 1997

3. The White Sox over the Cubs in 1906

4. True

5. The Yankees over the Brooklyn Dodgers in 1956

6. The NL Boston Braves beat the AL Philadelphia Athletics in 1914 and the Red Sox beat the Phillies in 1915.

7. The A's beat the Dodgers in 1974.

8. Twins over Cards in 1987

9. The Royals over the Cards in 1985 — after Interstate Highway I-70

10. The Orioles over the Phillies in 1983 — after Interstate Highway I-95

Sec. 82 Row E Seat 17

Enter Gate B

"I never say 'seven-fifteen' anymore. Now I say 'quarter after seven.'"

–Former pitcher Al Downing, who served up Hank Aaron's record–breaking 715th homer

HEADLINES

Give the year for each.

1. QUAKE HALTS SERIES
2. LIGHTS GO ON AT WRIGLEY
3. YANKS HOLD LOU GEHRIG APPRECIATION DAY
4. AARON HITS NUMBER 755
5. TED WILLIAMS HOMERS IN FINAL AT-BAT
6. BILLY MARTIN DIES IN ACCIDENT
7. IT'S OFFICIAL — BREWERS TO MOVE TO NATIONAL LEAGUE
8. WILLIE MAYS TRADED TO METS
9. PETE ROSE BANNED FROM BASEBALL
10. DODGERS BEAT A'S ON GIBSON HOMER

FULL SEASON

Sec. 17
Row K
Seat 22
Gate F

"Good pitching always stops good hitting and vice versa."

–Ex-Pirates pitcher Bob Veale

ANSWERS

1. 1989
2. 1988
3. 1939
4. 1976
5. 1960
6. 1989
7. 1997
8. 1972
9. 1989
10. 1988

Sec. 07

Row 19

Seat 12

Enter
Gate C
Upper Tier

"Airplanes may kill you, but they ain't likely to hurt you."

–Hall of Fame pitcher Satchel Paige

FULL SEASON TICKET

MULTI-SPORT

The following each describe an athlete who made a mark
in two or more sports, one of which was baseball.

1. He played for the Dodgers, Cubs and Celtics, but became
   better known as a TV star.

2. He was an outfielder for the New York Giants in 1944-45
   and a halfback for the New York Giants in 1945-56.

3. In addition to his stints with the Reds, Braves and Giants,
   he was named AP Male Athlete of the Half-Century in 1950.

4. He played parts of three seasons with the Blue Jays but had
   more success with the Boston Celtics.

5. Celtics teammate Bill Russell said this two-sport star had to
   wait four weeks after the season ended before pitching for the
   Red Sox because "it took him that long to get out of shape."

6. An All-America basketball star at Duke who played briefly
   for the NBA Pistons, he moved on to baseball and won the
   MVP for the 1960 World Champion Pirates.

7. He played for both the Braves and the NFL Atlanta Falcons
   in the early '90s.

8. He won the Heisman Trophy and was drafted number one
   overall by the Tampa Bay Buccaneers but initially chose to
   turn pro in baseball.

9. He won the Heisman as an Ohio State junior and later
   played professionally for both the Pirates and the NFL
   Washington Redskins.

10. He was captain of the University of Illinois basketball team in
    1936-37, but ended up having a Hall of Fame baseball career,
    primarily with the Indians.

ANSWERS

1. Chuck Connors, *The Rifleman*
2. Steve "Flip" Filipowicz
3. Jim Thorpe
4. Danny Ainge
5. Gene Conley
6. Dick Groat
7. Deion Sanders
8. Bo Jackson
9. Vic Janowicz
10. Lou Boudreau

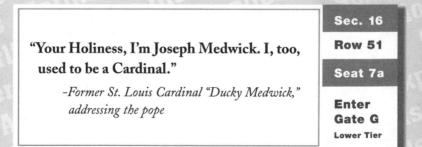

"Your Holiness, I'm Joseph Medwick. I, too, used to be a Cardinal."

–Former St. Louis Cardinal "Ducky Medwick," addressing the pope

Sec. 16

Row 51

Seat 7a

Enter Gate G
Lower Tier

TEAMS ON THE MOVE

1. Two different still existing franchises were previously known as the Washington Senators. To which city did each move?

2. Despite never moving more than a county away, which team has been known by three different geographical names?

3. What was the last major league team of the 1900s to relocate to another city?

4. Jim Bouton's legendary book *Ball Four* dealt largely with the exploits of an expansion team that spent only a single season in its city of origin. What was the team?

5. Who was the only player to play for the Braves in each of the three cities they called home?

6. It took more than half a century but the National League finally won the battle for Philadelphia's fans when the Athletics moved to which city?

7. Which American League city was without a team for the 1968 season following the move of a previous franchise and preceding the debut of an expansion team?

8. What is the only modern major league team to move from one league to the other?

9. Which team became the Baltimore Orioles in 1954?

10. What season was the first in California for both the Giants and the Dodgers?

ANSWERS

1. The original Senators became the Minnesota Twins in 1961 and the "new" Senators became the Texas Rangers in 1972.

2. The Los Angeles-California-Anaheim Angels

3. The Senators-come-Rangers in 1972

4. The 1969 Seattle Pilots became the Milwaukee Brewers the following season.

5. Eddie Mathews

6. Kansas City

7. Kansas City

8. The Milwaukee Brewers left the American League and began play in the National League in the 1998 season.

9. The St. Louis Browns

10. 1958

Sec. 07

Row 19

Seat 12

Enter
Gate C
Upper Tier

FULL SEASON TICKET

"The Mets just had their first .500 or better April since July of 1992."

-Hall of Famer and broadcaster Ralph Kiner

IT'S ALL RELATIVE II

1. Who is the better known sister of Randy Moffitt, who pitched for the Giants in the '70s?

2. Former Cubs and Royals infielder Pete LaCock is the son of which TV personality?

3. Did Pete Rose Jr. ever make it to the bigs?

4. Which Mets/Phillies pitcher of the '70s and '80s saw his son become a country music star in the '90s?

5. Name the first brothers to oppose each other as rookie starting pitchers.

6. What did Paul and Lloyd Waner of the Pirates do on September 15, 1938 that no brothers have done before or since?

7. Who are the only two brothers to both throw no-hitters in the majors (one of them throwing two)?

8. What made Senators owner Clark Griffith's trade of Joe Cronin to the Red Sox in 1934 especially noteworthy?

9. Name the only two brothers to win Cy Young Awards in the 1900s.

10. Who were the brothers who finished first and second for the NL batting title in 1966?

ANSWERS

1. Billie Jean King

2. Peter Marshall, host of the original *Hollywood Squares*.

3. Yes — For 11 games with the Reds in 1997

4. Tug McGraw, father of Tim

5. Greg (Cubs) and Mike (Phillies) Maddux in 1986 —
   The Cubs won 8-3.

6. Hit back-to-back homers (off Cliff Melton in a victory over
   the Giants)

7. Bob (Cards over Phillies in 1978, Cards over Expos in 1983)
   and Ken (Astros over Braves in 1979) Forsch

8. Cronin was married to Griffith's daughter.

9. Jim (Twins, 1970) and Gaylord (Indians, 1972) Perry

10. The Pirates' Matty (.342) and the Braves' Felipe (.327) Alou

FULL SEASON

Sec. 17
Row K
Seat 22
Gate F

"I don't know. I'm not in shape yet."

-Yogi Berra, when asked about his cap size

CLOSING IT OUT

What was the very last major league team
each of the following played for?

1. Roger Maris
2. Reggie Jackson
3. Babe Ruth
4. Henry Aaron
5. Dick Allen
6. Steve Carlton
7. Phil Niekro
8. Bobby Bonds
9. Jimmy Piersall
10. John Kruk

Sec.	Row	Seat
82	E	17

Enter Gate B

"It's like watching Mario Andretti park a car."

–Ralph Kiner, on Phil Niekro's knuckleball

ANSWERS

1. Cardinals — 1968
2. A's — 1987
3. Boston Braves — 1935
4. Milwaukee Brewers — 1976
5. A's — 1977
6. Twins — 1988
7. Braves — 1987
8. Cubs — 1981
9. Angels — 1967
10. White Sox — 1995

Sec. **82** Row **E** Seat **17**

Enter Gate B

"I've been called everything but my name."

-Umpire Dave Phillips

LAST OF ALL

1. Who was the last pitcher of the 1900s to win 30 games in a season?

2. Who was the last of the New York Giants still playing in San Francisco?

3. Who was the last of the Brooklyn Dodgers still playing in Los Angeles?

4. Who was the last original New York Met to leave the team?

5. Who were the last brothers to be starting pitchers for the same team on both ends of a doubleheader?

6. What was the last team of the 16 that played in 1903 (the year of the first World Series) to win a World Series?

7. Who was the last active player to have played for the original Washington Senators?

8. Who was the last player from the Negro Leagues to play for a major league team?

9. Who appeared in the final Brooklyn Dodgers-New York Giants game and was still in uniform at century's end as a coach?

10. Who was the last active major-leaguer to have been managed by Casey Stengel?

ANSWERS

1. Denny McLain won 31 for the Tigers in 1968.

2. Willie Mays, 1972

3. Don Drysdale, 1969

4. Ed Kranepool, 1979

5. Jim and Gaylord Perry for the Indians in 1974

6. The Phillies in 1980

7. Jim Kaat — He broke in with the Senators in 1959 and closed it out with the Cards in 1983.

8. Henry Aaron — He played for the Indianapolis Clowns in 1952, made it to the Braves in 1954 and closed it out with the Brewers in 1976.

9. Yankees bench coach Don Zimmer — He was a Dodger in 1957 and got into the game as a pinch hitter.

10. Tug McGraw — He broke in with the '65 Mets, Stengel's final year as a manager, and closed it out with the Phillies in 1984.